The Thinking Tree

GENESIS DEVOTIONAL JOURNAL

Illustrated by: Rachel Charity Brown

In collaboration with:

Susannah Autumn Brown & Sarah Janisse Brown

FUNSCHOOLING.COM

The Dyslexie Font is used to improve the experience for struggling readers.

INSTRUCTIONS: Choose the Bible translation of your choice and read a chapter each day. Follow the prompts on each page, and use gel pens and colored pencils to complete the activities. Tips: Listen to a sermon on each chapter, by your favorite Bible teacher, while coloring the illustrations. The artwork was created by Rachel Brown, age 18, add your own artwork to each page.

READ GENESIS CHAPTER 1

Copy your favorite verse from this chapter:

Create a comic to illustrate the story:

People & Places to pray for today:

1.________________
2.________________
3.________________
4.________________
5.________________
6.________________
7.________________
8.________________
9.________________
10.______________

Write your prayers & thoughts:

____
____
____
____
____

READ GENESIS CHAPTER 2

Copy your favorite verse from this chapter:

Create a comic to illustrate the story:

People & Places to pray for today:

1.________________
2.________________
3.________________
4.________________
5.________________
6.________________
7.________________
8.________________
9.________________
10.______________

Write your prayers & thoughts:

READ GENESIS CHAPTER 3

Copy your favorite verse from this chapter:

____

____

____

____

____

Create a comic to illustrate the story:

People & Places
to pray for today:

1.________________
2.________________
3.________________
4.________________
5.________________
6.________________
7.________________
8.________________
9.________________
10.______________

Write your prayers & thoughts:

READ GENESIS CHAPTER 4

Copy your favorite verse from this chapter:

Create a comic to illustrate the story:

People & Places to pray for today:

1._______________
2._______________
3._______________
4._______________
5._______________
6._______________
7._______________
8._______________
9._______________
10.______________

Write your prayers & thoughts:

READ GENESIS CHAPTER 5

Copy your favorite verse from this chapter:

Create a comic to illustrate the story:

What was the most important or interesting thing in this chapter?

People & Places to pray for today:

1._______________
2._______________
3._______________
4._______________
5._______________
6._______________
7._______________
8._______________
9._______________
10.______________

Write your prayers & thoughts:

READ GENESIS CHAPTER 6

Copy your favorite verse from this chapter:

Create a comic to illustrate the story:

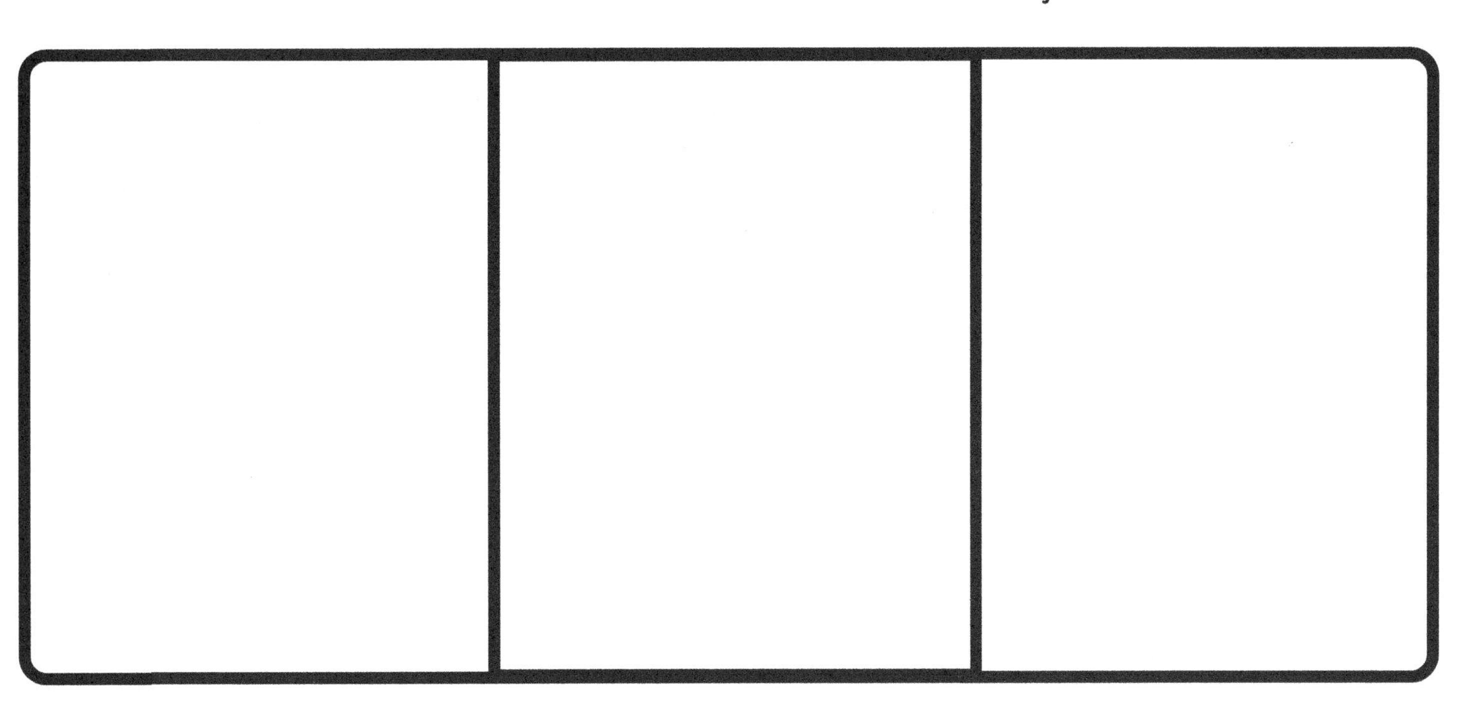

Write your prayers & thoughts:

READ GENESIS CHAPTER 7

Copy your favorite verse from this chapter:

Create a comic to illustrate the story:

What was the most important or interesting thing in this chapter?

People & Places to pray for today:

1.______________

2.______________

3.______________

4.______________

5.______________

6.______________

7.______________

8.______________

9.______________

10.______________

Write your prayers & thoughts:

READ GENESIS CHAPTER 8

Copy your favorite verse from this chapter:

Create a comic to illustrate the story:

What was the most important or interesting thing in this chapter?

People & Places to pray for today:

1.______________
2.______________
3.______________
4.______________
5.______________
6.______________
7.______________
8.______________
9.______________
10.______________

Write your prayers & thoughts:

READ GENESIS CHAPTER 9

Copy your favorite verse from this chapter:

Create a comic to illustrate the story:

What was the most important or interesting thing in this chapter?

People & Places to pray for today:

1._______________
2._______________
3._______________
4._______________
5._______________
6._______________
7._______________
8._______________
9._______________
10.______________

Write your prayers & thoughts:

READ GENESIS CHAPTER 10

Copy your favorite verse from this chapter:

Create a comic to illustrate the story:

What was the most important or interesting thing in this chapter?

People & Places to pray for today:

1.______________

2.______________

3.______________

4.______________

5.______________

6.______________

7.______________

8.______________

9.______________

10.______________

Write your prayers & thoughts:

READ GENESIS CHAPTER 11

Copy your favorite verse from this chapter:

Create a comic to illustrate the story:

People & Places
to pray for today:

1.________________
2.________________
3.________________
4.________________
5.________________
6.________________
7.________________
8.________________
9.________________
10._______________

Write your prayers & thoughts:

READ GENESIS CHAPTER 12

Copy your favorite verse from this chapter:

Create a comic to illustrate the story:

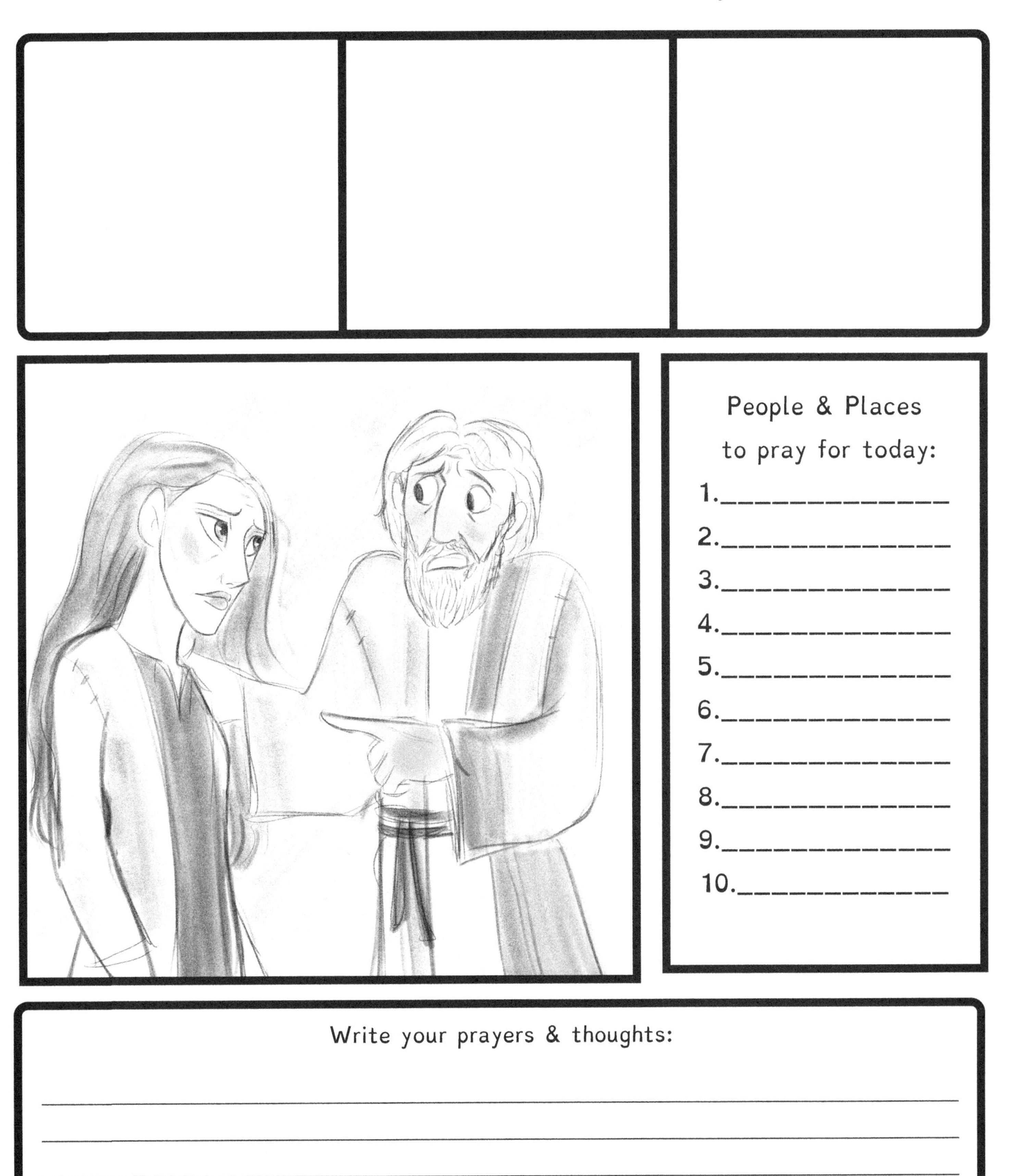

People & Places
to pray for today:

1.______________
2.______________
3.______________
4.______________
5.______________
6.______________
7.______________
8.______________
9.______________
10.____________

Write your prayers & thoughts:

READ GENESIS CHAPTER 13

Copy your favorite verse from this chapter:

Create a comic to illustrate the story:

People & Places to pray for today:

1.______________

2.______________

3.______________

4.______________

5.______________

6.______________

7.______________

8.______________

9.______________

10.______________

Write your prayers & thoughts:

READ GENESIS CHAPTER 14

Copy your favorite verse from this chapter:

Create a comic to illustrate the story:

What was the most important or interesting thing in this chapter?

People & Places to pray for today:

1._______________
2._______________
3._______________
4._______________
5._______________
6._______________
7._______________
8._______________
9._______________
10.______________

Write your prayers & thoughts:

READ GENESIS CHAPTER 15

Copy your favorite verse from this chapter:

Create a comic to illustrate the story:

What was the most important or interesting thing in this chapter?

People & Places to pray for today:

1.______________

2.______________

3.______________

4.______________

5.______________

6.______________

7.______________

8.______________

9.______________

10.______________

Write your prayers & thoughts:

READ GENESIS CHAPTER 16

Copy your favorite verse from this chapter:

Create a comic to illustrate the story:

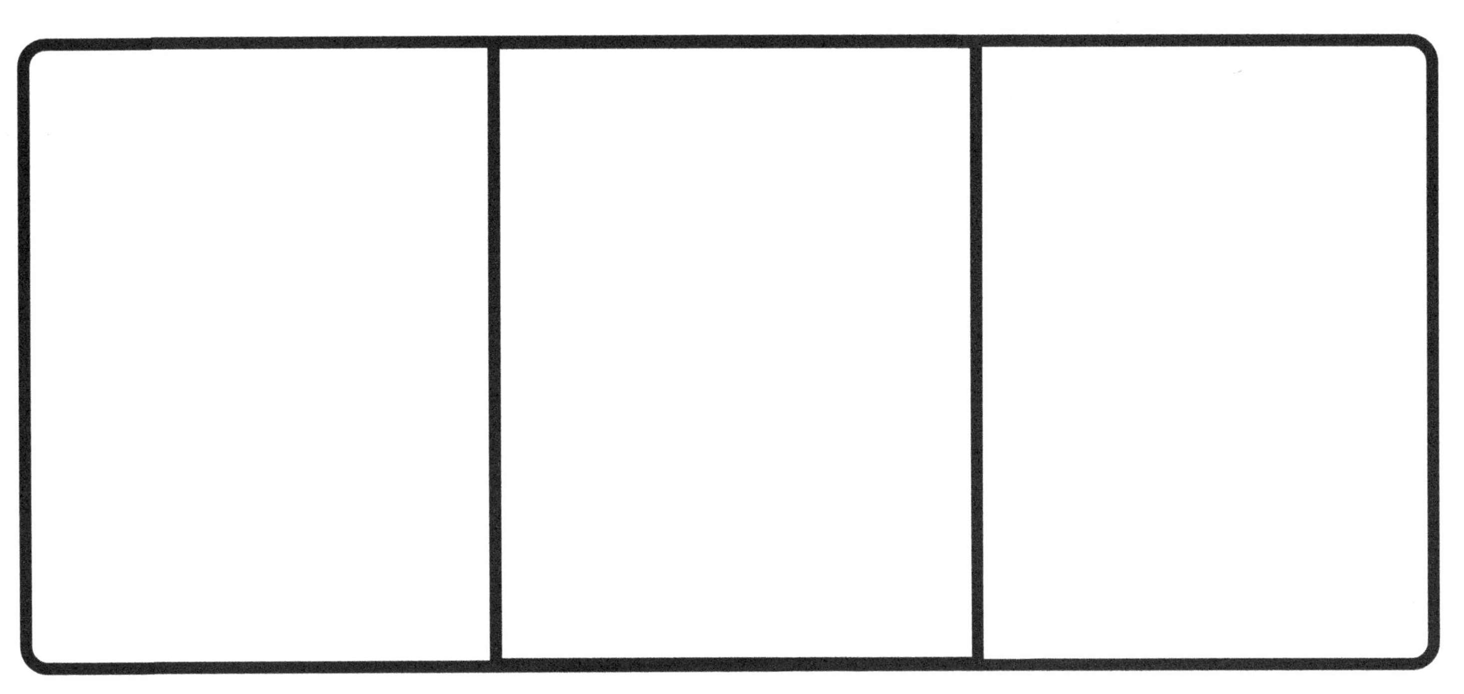

Write your prayers & thoughts:

READ GENESIS CHAPTER 17

Copy your favorite verse from this chapter:

Create a comic to illustrate the story:

What was the most important or interesting thing in this chapter?

People & Places to pray for today:

1.______________
2.______________
3.______________
4.______________
5.______________
6.______________
7.______________
8.______________
9.______________
10.______________

Write your prayers & thoughts:

READ GENESIS CHAPTER 18

Copy your favorite verse from this chapter:

Create a comic to illustrate the story:

People & Places
to pray for today:

1.______________
2.______________
3.______________
4.______________
5.______________
6.______________
7.______________
8.______________
9.______________
10.____________

Write your prayers & thoughts:

READ GENESIS CHAPTER 19

Copy your favorite verse from this chapter:

Create a comic to illustrate the story:

People & Places to pray for today:

1.______________

2.______________

3.______________

4.______________

5.______________

6.______________

7.______________

8.______________

9.______________

10.______________

Write your prayers & thoughts:

____

____

____

____

____

READ GENESIS CHAPTER 20

Copy your favorite verse from this chapter:

Create a comic to illustrate the story:

What was the most important or interesting thing in this chapter?

People & Places to pray for today:

1.______________
2.______________
3.______________
4.______________
5.______________
6.______________
7.______________
8.______________
9.______________
10.______________

Write your prayers & thoughts:

READ GENESIS CHAPTER 21

Copy your favorite verse from this chapter:

Create a comic to illustrate the story:

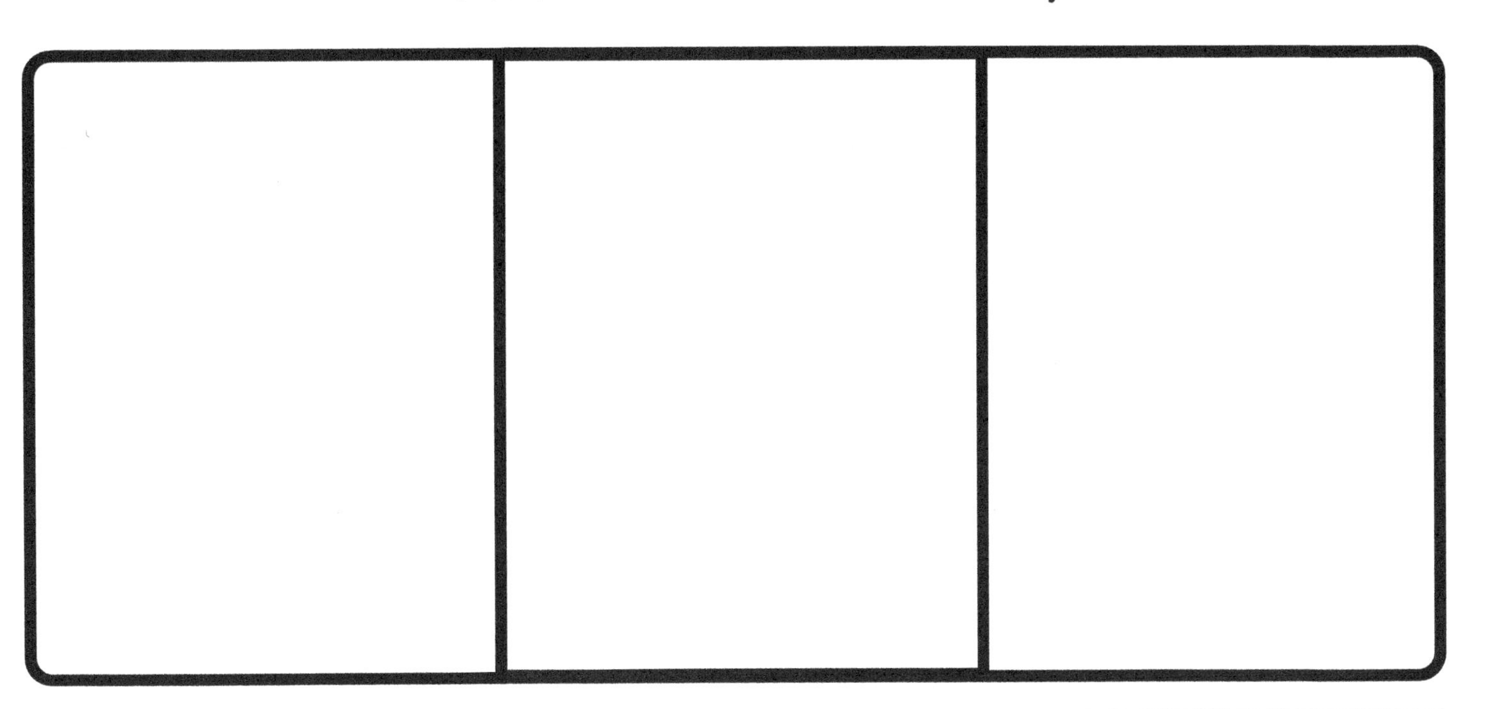

Write your prayers & thoughts:

READ GENESIS CHAPTER 22

Copy your favorite verse from this chapter:

Create a comic to illustrate the story:

What was the most important or interesting thing in this chapter?

People & Places to pray for today:

1.______________
2.______________
3.______________
4.______________
5.______________
6.______________
7.______________
8.______________
9.______________
10.______________

Write your prayers & thoughts:

READ GENESIS CHAPTER 23

Copy your favorite verse from this chapter:

Create a comic to illustrate the story:

What was the most important or interesting thing in this chapter?

People & Places to pray for today:

1.______________

2.______________

3.______________

4.______________

5.______________

6.______________

7.______________

8.______________

9.______________

10.______________

Write your prayers & thoughts:

READ GENESIS CHAPTER 24

Copy your favorite verse from this chapter:

Create a comic to illustrate the story:

Write your prayers & thoughts:

READ GENESIS CHAPTER 25

Copy your favorite verse from this chapter:

Create a comic to illustrate the story:

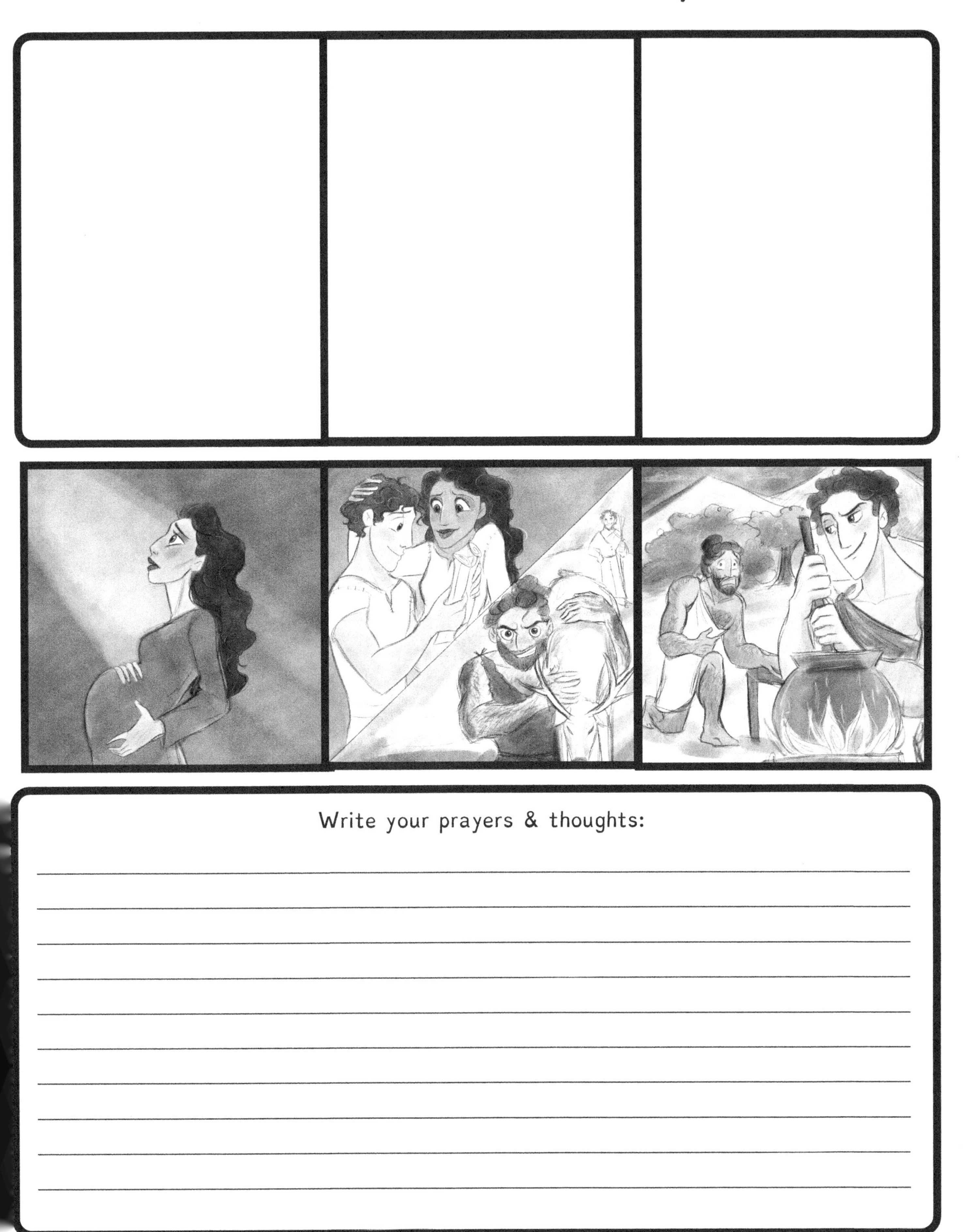

Write your prayers & thoughts:

READ GENESIS CHAPTER 26

Copy your favorite verse from this chapter:

Create a comic to illustrate the story:

What was the most important or interesting thing in this chapter?

People & Places to pray for today:

1.________________
2.________________
3.________________
4.________________
5.________________
6.________________
7.________________
8.________________
9.________________
10.______________

Write your prayers & thoughts:

READ GENESIS CHAPTER 27

Copy your favorite verse from this chapter:

Create a comic to illustrate the story:

People & Places to pray for today:

1.________________
2.________________
3.________________
4.________________
5.________________
6.________________
7.________________
8.________________
9.________________
10._______________

Write your prayers & thoughts:

READ GENESIS CHAPTER 28

Copy your favorite verse from this chapter:

Create a comic to illustrate the story:

People & Places
to pray for today:

1.______________

2.______________

3.______________

4.______________

5.______________

6.______________

7.______________

8.______________

9.______________

10.____________

Write your prayers & thoughts:

READ GENESIS CHAPTER 29

Copy your favorite verse from this chapter:

Create a comic to illustrate the story:

People & Places to pray for today:

1.______________

2.______________

3.______________

4.______________

5.______________

6.______________

7.______________

8.______________

9.______________

10.______________

Write your prayers & thoughts:

READ GENESIS CHAPTER 30

Copy your favorite verse from this chapter:

Create a comic to illustrate the story:

What was the most important or interesting thing in this chapter?

People & Places to pray for today:

1.______________
2.______________
3.______________
4.______________
5.______________
6.______________
7.______________
8.______________
9.______________
10.______________

Write your prayers & thoughts:

READ GENESIS CHAPTER 31

Copy your favorite verse from this chapter:

Create a comic to illustrate the story:

What was the most important or interesting thing in this chapter?

People & Places to pray for today:

1.______________
2.______________
3.______________
4.______________
5.______________
6.______________
7.______________
8.______________
9.______________
10.______________

Write your prayers & thoughts:

READ GENESIS CHAPTER 32

Copy your favorite verse from this chapter:

Create a comic to illustrate the story:

What was the most important
or interesting thing in this chapter?

People & Places
to pray for today:

1.______________
2.______________
3.______________
4.______________
5.______________
6.______________
7.______________
8.______________
9.______________
10.______________

Write your prayers & thoughts:

READ GENESIS CHAPTER 33

Copy your favorite verse from this chapter:

Create a comic to illustrate the story:

What was the most important or interesting thing in this chapter?

People & Places to pray for today:

1.______________
2.______________
3.______________
4.______________
5.______________
6.______________
7.______________
8.______________
9.______________
10.______________

Write your prayers & thoughts:

READ GENESIS CHAPTER 34

Copy your favorite verse from this chapter:

Create a comic to illustrate the story:

People & Places
to pray for today:

1.______________
2.______________
3.______________
4.______________
5.______________
6.______________
7.______________
8.______________
9.______________
10.______________

Write your prayers & thoughts:

____
____
____
____
____

READ GENESIS CHAPTER 35

Copy your favorite verse from this chapter:

Create a comic to illustrate the story:

People & Places to pray for today:

1.______________
2.______________
3.______________
4.______________
5.______________
6.______________
7.______________
8.______________
9.______________
10.______________

Write your prayers & thoughts:

READ GENESIS CHAPTER 36

Copy your favorite verse from this chapter:

Create a comic to illustrate the story:

What was the most important or interesting thing in this chapter?

People & Places to pray for today:

1.______________
2.______________
3.______________
4.______________
5.______________
6.______________
7.______________
8.______________
9.______________
10.______________

Write your prayers & thoughts:

READ GENESIS CHAPTER 37

Copy your favorite verse from this chapter:

Create a comic to illustrate the story:

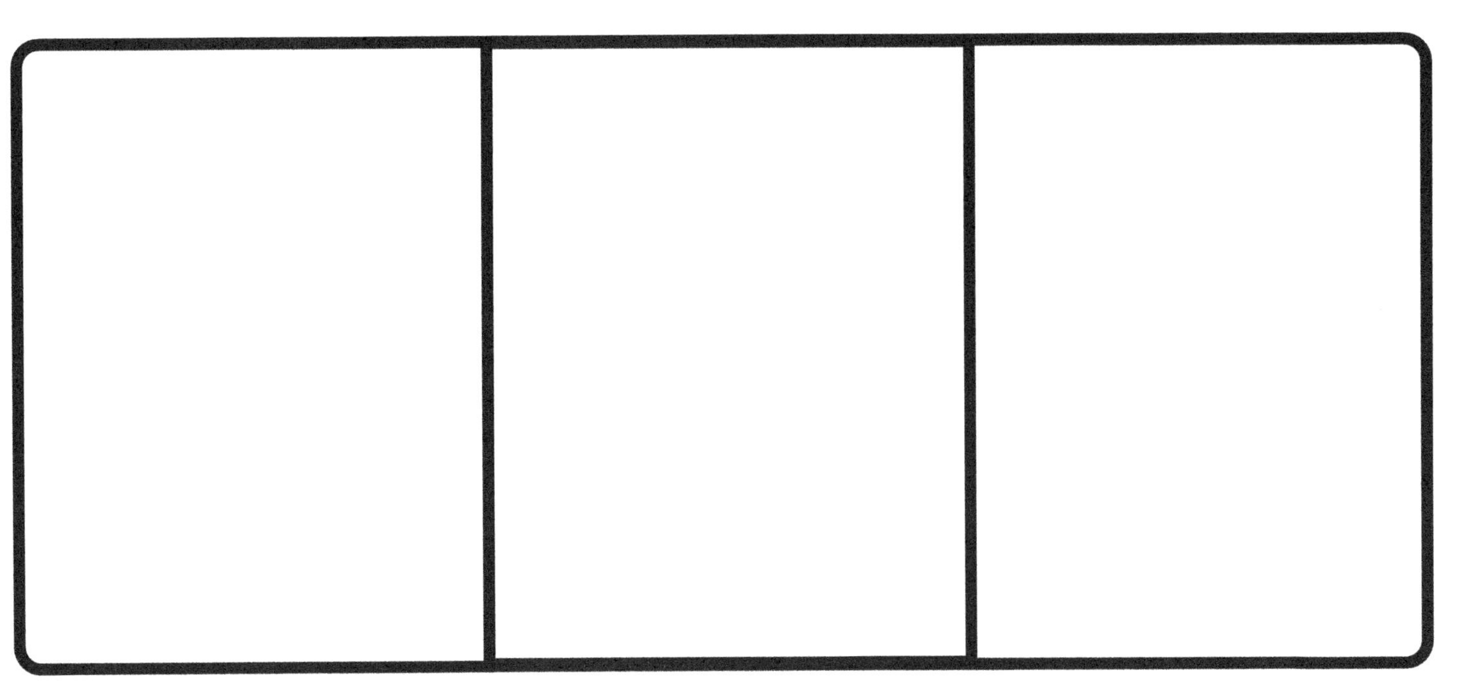

Write your prayers & thoughts:

READ GENESIS CHAPTER 37

Copy your favorite verse from this chapter:

Create a comic to illustrate the story:

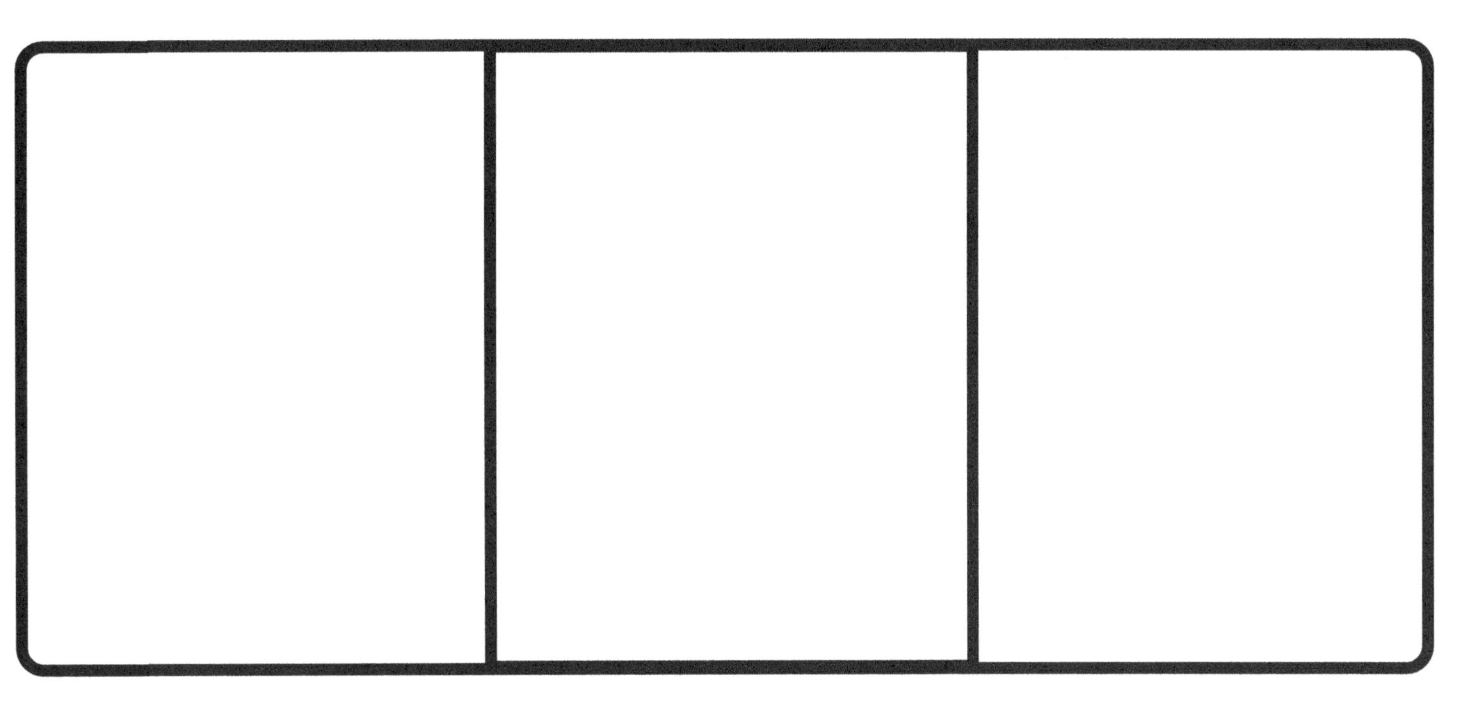

Write your prayers & thoughts:

READ GENESIS CHAPTER 38

Copy your favorite verse from this chapter:

Create a comic to illustrate the story:

READ GENESIS CHAPTER 39

Copy your favorite verse from this chapter:

Create a comic to illustrate the story:

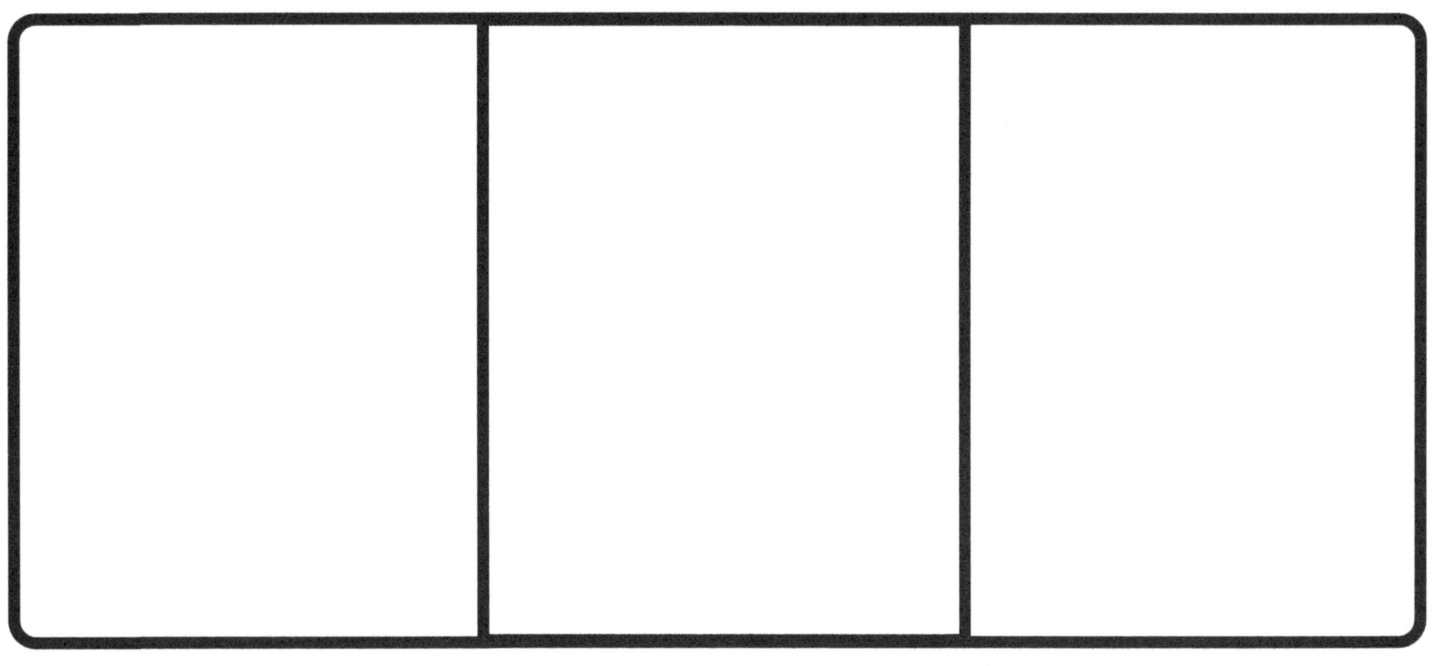

Write your prayers & thoughts:

READ GENESIS CHAPTER 40

Copy your favorite verse from this chapter:

Create a comic to illustrate the story:

READ GENESIS CHAPTER 41

Copy your favorite verse from this chapter:

Create a comic to illustrate the story:

People & Places
to pray for today:

1.______________
2.______________
3.______________
4.______________
5.______________
6.______________
7.______________
8.______________
9.______________
10.______________

Write your prayers & thoughts:

____
____
____
____
____

READ GENESIS CHAPTER 42

Copy your favorite verse from this chapter:

Create a comic to illustrate the story:

People & Places to pray for today:

1.______________
2.______________
3.______________
4.______________
5.______________
6.______________
7.______________
8.______________
9.______________
10.______________

Write your prayers & thoughts:

READ GENESIS CHAPTER 43

Copy your favorite verse from this chapter:

Create a comic to illustrate the story:

What was the most important or interesting thing in this chapter?

People & Places to pray for today:

1.______________

2.______________

3.______________

4.______________

5.______________

6.______________

7.______________

8.______________

9.______________

10.______________

Write your prayers & thoughts:

READ GENESIS CHAPTER 44

Copy your favorite verse from this chapter:

Create a comic to illustrate the story:

What was the most important or interesting thing in this chapter?

People & Places to pray for today:

1.______________

2.______________

3.______________

4.______________

5.______________

6.______________

7.______________

8.______________

9.______________

10.______________

Write your prayers & thoughts:

READ GENESIS CHAPTER 45

Copy your favorite verse from this chapter:

Create a comic to illustrate the story:

What was the most important or interesting thing in this chapter?

People & Places to pray for today:

1._______________

2._______________

3._______________

4._______________

5._______________

6._______________

7._______________

8._______________

9._______________

10.______________

Write your prayers & thoughts:

READ GENESIS CHAPTER 46

Copy your favorite verse from this chapter:

Create a comic to illustrate the story:

What was the most important or interesting thing in this chapter?

People & Places to pray for today:

1.______________
2.______________
3.______________
4.______________
5.______________
6.______________
7.______________
8.______________
9.______________
10.______________

Write your prayers & thoughts:

READ GENESIS CHAPTER 47

Copy your favorite verse from this chapter:

Create a comic to illustrate the story:

What was the most important or interesting thing in this chapter?

People & Places to pray for today:

1.______________

2.______________

3.______________

4.______________

5.______________

6.______________

7.______________

8.______________

9.______________

10.______________

Write your prayers & thoughts:

READ GENESIS CHAPTER 48

Copy your favorite verse from this chapter:

Create a comic to illustrate the story:

What was the most important or interesting thing in this chapter?

People & Places to pray for today:

1.______________
2.______________
3.______________
4.______________
5.______________
6.______________
7.______________
8.______________
9.______________
10.______________

Write your prayers & thoughts:

READ GENESIS CHAPTER 49

Copy your favorite verse from this chapter:

Create a comic to illustrate the story:

What was the most important or interesting thing in this chapter?

People & Places to pray for today:

1.______________
2.______________
3.______________
4.______________
5.______________
6.______________
7.______________
8.______________
9.______________
10.______________

Write your prayers & thoughts:

READ GENESIS CHAPTER 50

Copy your favorite verse from this chapter:

Create a comic to illustrate the story:

People & Places

to pray for today:

1.______________

2.______________

3.______________

4.______________

5.______________

6.______________

7.______________

8.______________

9.______________

10.______________

Write your prayers & thoughts:

NOTES

NOTES

NOTES

NOTES

NOTES

NOTES

NOTES

Made in the USA
Las Vegas, NV
30 June 2022